GOOD, GREEN JOBS

HOW BUSINESS IS PUTTING THE ENVIRONMENT TO WORK FOR CALIFORNIA

BY JOEL MAKOWER
Editor, *The Green Business Letter*

California Department of Conservation
1995

...nt of Conservation, Division
...A 95814; 800-RECYCLE

...ve. NW, Washington, DC

...vided under a grant (#5093-
203) from the California Department of Conservation in association with Keep California Beautiful, Inc.

PRINTED IN THE UNITED STATES OF AMERICA
ISBN 0–9505750–6–5

Cover design by Lisa Wood Design
Text design by Mary Ann W. Bruce Graphic Design
Printed on recycled paper using soy-based inks

Grateful appreciation and thanks are due to those who contributed to this project:

Kathleen Cronin, Department of Conservation; Terri Gray, Department of Conservation; Alan Green; Stuart Greenbaum, Greenbaum Public Relations; Margie Jewett, Department of Conservation; Marlene Mariani and Theresa Creech, Keep California Beautiful; Carol Nelson, Department of Conservation; Mariann Payne; Susan Sakakihara, Department of Conservation; and Patrick Tracey.

Contents

Foreword

by Governor Pete Wilson

California is once again on the leading edge of the next technological revolution. Just as the computer industry was nurtured and then flourished in California in the 1980s, environmental technology is poised to be a driving force in the economic growth of California in the 21st century.

California companies are already using environmental innovation to create new markets around the world. One section of this book profiles a number of companies' innovative solutions to environmental challenges, which show that the environment and job creation can, and do, coexist. Companies of all sizes and in all industries are beginning to recognize the growth potential of environmentally responsible methods of operation.

In response to these developments, new partnerships are being forged between private companies and a number of other entities, including energy utilities, nonprofits, communities, and even government regulators. At every level, formal and informal coalitions are finding better ways to conserve resources while increasing profits and jobs.

Californians are committed to clean air, clean water, and conserving the wondrous beauty found in every corner of our state; we are equally committed to economic growth. To do both effectively, we must *harness* the power of business, not hamstring it. We must intelligently manage the wealth of brain power, innovation, and resources with which the Golden State is so richly blessed.

This book is meant to highlight the growth potential of environmentally responsible innovations. I hope that you find it helpful and inspirational in putting the environment to work for your company.

PART ONE

Good Green Jobs

Good, Green Jobs

Jobs and the environment.

Not long ago, conventional wisdom had it that you could have either one or the other, but not both. Increasing the number of jobs meant generating more pollution and waste. Reducing pollution and waste meant doing less business — and fewer jobs.

We now know that both sides were wrong: job growth and environmental responsibility can go hand in hand. In many ways, they are inextricably linked.

When it comes to jobs and the environment, California faces unique challenges and opportunities. The challenges include creating and maintaining a clean environment by limiting or eliminating waste and pollution generated by homes, businesses, and motor vehicles, as well as by turning waste into resources to be used for new products. The challenge is made tougher by everyone's desire not to unduly burden individuals or companies in the process.

But those challenges present opportunities to create a vibrant new economic future through environmental technology and innovation. By turning a clean environment into a vehicle for creating jobs, we not only can address California's environmental challenges but also its economic ones. Reclaiming and reusing waste materials within California reduces the need to export those materials—as well as jobs—to other states and countries. In addition, by marketing the environmental technologies and expertise of California businesses around the country and around the world, we can tap a market whose potential is billions of dollars—and countless new jobs.

How to realize those dual benefits—a healthier environment and a healthier economy—is what this book is all about. In the pages that follow, you will learn:

- the potential for creating jobs through conservation, recycling, leaner production methods, and new environmental technologies;
- profiles of large and small California companies that are creating jobs through their environmental initiatives; and

- government, private-sector, and nonprofit organizations offering technological, financial, or informational assistance to help companies implement job-creating environmental initiatives.

The companies and organizations profiled in this publication represent only a handful of examples of a wide range of initiatives. Some have created jobs; others have kept jobs from disappearing or leaving the state. Some involve significant financial investments; others require minimal investments. Some business leaders did these things entirely on their own; others formed partnerships with government or nonprofit agencies.

Together, they represent a fraction of the potential jobs that can be created through conservation and environmental technology.

How Many Jobs?

The idea that recycling and other environmental technologies can create jobs is not just theory. A large body of evidence has demonstrated the job-creating power of "going green."

Jobs From Recycling

Consider recycling. The Institute for Local Self-Reliance in Washington, D.C., estimates that nine jobs are created for every 15,000 tons of solid waste recycled into a new product, and seven for the same amount of yard trimmings composted. By contrast, only two jobs are created for every 15,000 tons incinerated, and just one job for every 15,000 tons sent to landfills. According to a 1992 study for the California Integrated Waste Management Board, diverting 50% of the state's waste stream from landfills could lead to 40,000 or more new jobs in California by the year 2000, through processing recyclables and manufacturing recycled-content products.

Others have made their own assessments. For example:

- The city of San Jose estimated it could create 775 jobs by recycling 624,600 tons of materials, or 1 job per 805 tons.
- Massachusetts estimated in 1991 that one million tons of material recycled in the state contributed to the employment of 10,000 people, mostly in manufacturing.
- In Washington state, recycling created 2,050 manufacturing jobs in 1991 and 1992, while the sector overall lost 15,000 jobs.
- In Minnesota, six manufacturers using recyclable materials created 1,688 jobs, generating roughly $39 million in new wages.

- Alcoa estimates that at least 30,000 people in the United States are employed in aluminum recycling alone—twice as many as in aluminum production.
- Approximately 103,400 people are employed in firms that process recyclables or use them in manufacturing in the Northeast U.S., representing 2.7% of the approximately 3.8 million manufacturing jobs in the 10-state region.

Another benefit of recycling is the kinds of jobs it creates. According to the Worldwatch Institute: "Building waste-burning plants and manufacturing the machinery they use creates more *temporary* jobs than does building the more modestly equipped recycling centers. But recycling offers a larger number of *permanent* jobs in operations and maintenance activities." In New York City, for example, recycling creates far more jobs annually (between 390 and 580) than do either landfills (40 to 50) or incinerators (80 to 290).

Jobs From New Technologies

Recycling is by no means the only source of environmental jobs. Another way jobs are created is through new environmental technologies. These come in several categories:

- Technologies that reduce pollution coming from factories, farms, and motor vehicles
- Technologies that turn waste materials into the feedstocks of new products
- Technologies that clean up existing pollution
- Technologies that lead to less-wasteful production methods
- Technologies that lead to less-polluting products
- Technologies that lead to more efficient energy use

It is difficult to measure the number of jobs being created from such businesses, due to their diverse nature. And not all companies doing these things are necessarily creating new jobs.

For example, most California farmers are reducing or eliminating their use of pesticides, which are known to wash off farmlands and into the drinking water supply. And many factories in the state are using "pollution prevention" techniques, which reduce waste and pollution at the source rather than after they are created. Such measures may not increase employment, though there may be other benefits to Californians through cleaner air and water, reduced employee health risks, lower prices, and increased profits.

In addition, many of these new technologies, though promising, are unproven and not expected to create jobs for several years, following extensive research, development, and testing.

One measure of the potential of new environmental technologies is in the size of their worldwide market. For example, the Organization for Economic Cooperation and Development estimates that the international market for environmental goods and services is already more than $200 billion per year and will grow at 5.5% a year through the end of the century. The U.S. Congress's Office of Technology Assessment (OTA) estimates that the international environmental market could grow to $300 billion by the turn of the century. One study estimates that by 2010, the total worldwide market for energy-efficiency equipment and services will grow to about $250 billion a year.

The above statistics include only end-of-pipe pollution control, waste disposal, and remedial cleanup of pollution, says OTA. "The projected market would be much larger if cleaner production technologies and products were included, but there are no good projections of the potential size of this market," according to a 1994 report.

In the long term, says OTA, cleaner technology and production processes may have the potential to generate more export-related growth and jobs than conventional pollution control equipment. The shift toward cleaner production is likely to occur incrementally over the next 15 to 25 years, as manufacturers build new facilities or upgrade existing plants. There likely will be growing global demand for cleaner and more energy-efficient industrial facilities, including those for power generation, chemical processing, smelting, oil refining, papermaking, food processing, and product assembly. States and countries with firms that are competitive suppliers in these areas will benefit from the jobs and commerce generated from trade in capital equipment and related professional services.

Jobs Retained

Still another way that environmental initiatives create employment is by reducing or avoiding job loss through layoffs, plant closures, and business relocations. For example, some environmental initiatives allow older, less-efficient businesses or facilities to become more efficient and profitable, thereby avoiding having to lay off employees or shut down altogether.

Other initiatives help companies stay in business by making it easier to comply with environmental regulations through technical or financial assistance. Still others offer assistance for companies trying to develop or market environmental technologies, thereby helping them to grow into bigger companies with more employees.

Again, measuring the job-creating potential of these initiatives is difficult. For example, there are no statistics on the number of businesses that decide not to shut down or leave the state after receiving financial or technical assistance. It is also difficult to track the number of small environmental companies taking advantage of these programs with the aim of becoming much larger companies.

Most economists agree that helping small businesses grow is one of the most effective ways to create jobs. Small-business startups are the fastest-growing sector of the economy. Small companies employ half the country's work force and create two out of every three new jobs. By the year 2000, 85% of Americans will work in companies of 200 or fewer employees.

The Bottom Line

So, how many jobs can be created in California through recycling, new technologies, partnerships, and other environmental business initiatives? Based on the examples in this book—all of which are potentially replicable throughout the state—the potential jobs number in the hundreds of thousands. In addition, there is a multiplier effect, in which each growing business brings revenue—and jobs—to suppliers and subcontractors as well as generating tax revenue that contributes to additional economic activity.

Whatever the actual number of jobs created or saved, there is little question that "going green" can be as good for business as it is for the environment. Increasingly, companies are recognizing that all pollution and waste is lost profit—something that was purchased but which could not be sold.

By reducing waste and pollution, and by carefully conserving our state's resources, the companies profiled in this book have found that environmental responsibility is a path to sustainable growth, profits, and jobs.

That's good for business, good for the environment, and good for California.

PART TWO

The Profiles

Recycle-Ability

A successful recycling program requires sorting cans, bottles, newspapers, and other materials once they are collected. It takes a great deal of individual effort to do this. One result is that recycling is creating jobs for a variety of individuals who may otherwise have difficulty finding work.

The Organization

Ability Counts

The Opportunity

To provide job training for those who aren't readily employable in other industries.

The Challenge

Creating a cost-effective means to sort and process recyclables, often a highly labor-intensive job.

The Solution

Establish an environmental vocational education training center for the disabled.

Ability Counts began in the early 1980s as a vocational training center for the developmentally disabled. A commercial glass recycling program and a cardboard recycling program were established for the disabled to work with local waste haulers in the cities of Corona and Riverside.

The program ended when the city of Riverside chose an automated system for curbside recycling, but Ability Counts continued its own plastics recycling operation. With a grant from the California Department of Conservation, the company purchased a washing system that granulates plastic soft-drink bottles. It is planning to purchase an extruder to manufacture plastic pellets to make such products as carpeting, paint brushes, and sheeting for bubble-wrap packaging material.

The organization also recycles hangers for Nordstrom department store using a conveyer system that separates and repackages 20,000 hangers a day; the hangers are reused at the stores. "It saves Nordstrom a lot of money," says Chris Banducci, director of the company's plastics recycling operations. "It also saves landfill space and provides jobs for 50 people a day." A second plastics facility, which opened in 1994, employs 25 people in a public-private partnership with G&R Polymers.

The Bottom Line

Ability Counts now employs 250 employees, more than double the number of three years ago, and there were 40 additional job openings at the end of 1994, says Banducci.

The program breaks even, due in part to the $25 a day per employee contributed by the state Department of Rehabilitation. The remaining income comes from foundations and from the sale of recycled materials, which covers wages and overhead. In 1995, Banducci expects Ability Counts to be self-sustaining.

For More Information

Ability Counts
1651 Iowa Ave.
Riverside, CA 92501
909-734-6595
909-734-6590 (fax)

Can-Do Spirit

California has long led the nation in recycling beverage cans. But what happens to the millions of beer and soda cans collected every year? A typical aluminum can travels hundreds or even thousands of miles in the course of being recycled—creating new jobs all along the way.

The Company

Anheuser-Busch Recycling Corp.

The Opportunity

To facilitate the collection of used aluminum beverage containers and recycle them back into new beverage containers.

The Challenge

To efficiently collect cans from more than 150 recycling centers and curbside programs.

The Solution

Become a one-stop service center for large and small recycling operations.

Anheuser-Busch Recycling, a subsidiary of the giant brewery, handles 25% of all aluminum cans recycled in the United States. The Hayward plant buys cans redeemed by the public, as well as those from a large network of recycling centers. It is a major player in aluminum can recycling in the state, handling more than a billion cans in 1994.

Anheuser-Busch doesn't just collect cans. To make its network of recycling centers function smoothly, it provides them with a wide range of equipment and services: tractor trailers, can flatteners, densifiers, balers, and sorting lines, for example. It also provides consulting, marketing, and even advertising services to help small recycling operations grow.

The aluminum collected by the company is baled and shipped

to aluminum plants in Georgia, Kentucky, and Tennessee operated by aluminum giants Alcoa and Alcan. There it is turned into coils of "can sheet," which is purchased by Metal Container Corp., the Anheuser-Busch subsidiary that manufactures new cans; the company's California can-making plant is in Riverside. The manufactured cans are sent to Anheuser-Busch's two California breweries, in Fairfield and Van Nuys. The empy cans usually find their way back to Hayward.

All told, Anheuser-Busch recycles more aluminum cans than it sells into the marketplace each year, according to Web Gaskin, the recycling subsidiary's executive vice president and chief operating officer.

The Bottom Line

Anheuser-Busch Recycling Corp. employs only 10 people, but that's far from the whole employment picture, says Hayward plant manager Bill Richardson. Each of the 150 recycling centers it supports has employees, resulting in hundreds of additional jobs. "The recycling infrastructure just around beverage containers in California is massive," says Richardson. "It's huge."

For More Information

Anheuser Busch Recycling Corp.
30900 Huntwood Ave.
Hayward, CA 94544
510-471-4776
510-471-4899 (fax)

Motor Skills

Reducing the exhaust emissions of motor vehicles, industrial generators, electric utilities, and other sources is one of the big challenges to a cleaner California. Technologies that reduce engine emissions have a huge potential market.

The Company
Catalytica, Inc.

The Opportunity
To create clean combustion systems for manufacturing, power generation, transportation, and other uses.

The Challenge
Achieve the increasingly stringent levels of air emissions controls mandated by federal and state laws.

The Solution
Create new technologies that avoid the formation of pollution at the source.

Traditional pollution control has centered around devices that capture emissions as they are created. But as the costs associated with capturing pollutants rise, companies are turning to cost-effective pollution-prevention practices. Catalytica's pollution-prevention technologies, "catalysis," use highly specialized chemical processes to eliminate or minimize the formation or use of pollutants. Using computer-assisted molecular design tools, Catalytica engineers are able to modify manufacturing processes to more efficiently use raw materials, reduce energy requirements, and increase product yields.

One leading-edge product is a low-cost emissions monitor to help companies meet air-quality requirements. The monitor uses an array of sensors to measure oxides of nitrogen, carbon monoxide, and oxygen; measurements are transmitted electronically for continuous reading. By being able to measure a hot, wet sample, the system avoids the high costs associated with conventional analyzers.

Catalytica scientists also have devised a new method of turning plentiful natural gas into methanol, a discovery that could eventually make the clean-burning fuel a more economical alternative to gasoline. While research is still in the lab stage and has yet to result in a commercial process, industry experts have hailed the technique as an exciting breakthrough, saying it could dramatically increase methanol production. Said one industry expert: Catalytica's discovery "has been one of the Holy Grails in this area."

Catalytica has formed partnerships with companies in several industries to commercialize its processes. For example, a catalyst that enables natural gas turbines to emit fewer nitrogen oxides was developed with a Japanese company, Tanaka. Working with Genzyme, a Boston-area biotech company, Catalytica is developing pollution-reducing chemicals for sale to drug companies. All told, Catalytica has more than 90 U.S. and 600 foreign patent applications.

The Bottom Line

Since 1985, Catalytica has roughly doubled in size to just under 100 employees, including 20 in a plant in economically troubled East Palo Alto, which the company opened in 1993. As Catalytica's technologies mature, there is high potential for additional growth, both within the company and within other companies with which Catalytica forms partnerships.

For More Information

Catalytica, Inc.
430 Ferguson Dr.
Mountain View, CA 94043
415-940-3000
415-960-0127 (fax)

Power Partners

Older factories can't always compete with newer ones that use only a fraction as much energy to produce identical goods. There may appear to be little choice but to close the older plant and shift production to a newer one. But there are other solutions that can help the environment while keeping jobs from being lost.

The Company

Chinet Company

The Opportunity

To turn an older, inefficient plant into an efficient one, increasing productivity and saving a factory slated to close.

The Challenge

Generate energy-efficiency savings without a massive capital investment by the parent company.

The Solution

Form a partnership with the local electric utility.

The Connecticut-based company's 35-year-old Sacramento plant manufactures paper plates sold under the Chinet brand. As one of the company's oldest plants, it used outmoded machines and technologies that caused it to be far less productive or efficient as other facilities making the same products. In 1992, Connecticut-based Royal Packaging Industries, the parent company, had put the Sacramento plant's management on notice that it was considering shutting the plant down, laying off the company's approximately 250 employees.

For several months before that notice, officials at the Sacramento plant had been talking to energy-efficiency specialists at Sacramento Municipal Utility District, or SMUD, the local electric utility. SMUD energy specialist Doug Norwood was part of a team working with the plant to make it more energy efficient.

"We were seeing a lot of companies leave not just Sacramento, but California, because of the economic climate," says Norwood. "We have a lot of old industry in Sacramento. If it's part of a large, nationwide company, the Sacramento plant always seems to be the oldest, least-efficient plant. They look at their operation and say, 'Where are we losing money?' And often, it's in Sacramento. So, we've approached our largest customers to ask, 'How can we help you become more efficient?'"

In the case of Chinet, SMUD provided $277,500 in rebates for the purchase of technology that permitted Chinet to speed up its manufacturing machines. It also provided more than $1 million in low-cost financing for the purchase of a new pulp processor that allowed Chinet to use cheaper raw materials.

The Bottom Line

The plant remains open, largely because of the upgrades, though Royal Packaging Industries officials say restructuring and other strategic factors were also involved. As a result of the new efficiency measures, Chinet increased production per machine by 58% and reduced energy use per ton of material by 20%. The new pulping machine has reduced the cost of feed paper stock from $200 a ton to $80 a ton. "The plant is now making as many plates using six machines as they used to get out of 14," says Norwood.

Only about 55 employees now work in the plant, though that number is likely to rise during 1995, as the company puts more of its idle machinery back into operation, according to W. Brian Smith, the plant manager. Says Doug Norwood: "It's a real success story."

For More Information

Chinet Company
8450 Gerber Rd.
Sacramento, CA 95828
916-689-2020
916-689-0811 (fax)

Home, Green Home

Attracting businesses and jobs is the goal of nearly every city and county. In Berkeley, the goal is to lure environment-minded businesses, which city officials believe will provide above-average job growth and position the region for economic vitality well into the 21st century.

The Organization

City of Berkeley

The Opportunity

To attract business to the city of Berkeley and the East Bay, based on an established network of existing enterprises, technical expertise, and other resources.

The Challenge

To provide incentives and eliminate barriers for companies to locate or relocate in Berkeley, as well as support existing area businesses whose products or services benefit the environment.

The Solution

Create a "Green Valley," modeled loosely after Silicon Valley's cluster of high-tech businesses.

That's the ambitious goal of the Berkeley Community Development Department, which sees the environmental business sector as an area of great potential growth that can bring jobs and revenues to the city.

With the backing of the city council to target environmental businesses, city officials have compiled an inventory of 125 environment-related businesses already operating in Berkeley, ranging from recycling operations to environmental engineering and clean-up consultants. Copies of the inventory were sent to all 125 companies to help them communicate more effectively among themselves. Officials also rezoned part of the city to preserve space for manufacturing and retail businesses, obtained state designation of Oakland as one of the first Recycled Market Development Zones in the state, and assisted several environmental businesses to find sites, expedite permits, or obtain loans or grants. Future plans include expanding training and retraining of the local work force for jobs in environmental businesses and facilitating relationships between local businesses and experts at the University of California and Lawrence Berkeley Laboratory.

"We think that Berkeley is very well positioned to nurture this area of economic activity, given the large number of existing firms and organizations, the reputation of the city and its residents for environmental leadership, and the contributions of the university, Lawrence Berkeley Lab, and other local institutions," says Neil S. Mayer, the city's director of community development.

The Bottom Line

A University of California study found that between 1985 and 1990, there was a 33% increase in the "environmental economy" in Alameda County, while jobs countywide grew by 14%. The push for a "Green Valley" could continue or enhance that job growth.

The city's effort already is beginning to pay off. Several companies have relocated to Berkeley, lured by the removal of barriers to setting up business they had faced in other areas. In 1994, the "Green Valley" notion caught the attention of a director of the White House Office on Environmental Policy, who toured several area businesses and praised the city's effort.

For More Information

Community Development Department
City of Berkeley
2180 Milvia St., 2nd Fl.
Berkeley, CA 94704
510-644-6073
510-644-8678 (fax)

Logging In Profits

What do you do when a local industry runs into trouble? Some towns quietly fade into depression, lacking alternative industries. But in the logging town of Arcata, local entrepreneurs have made profits and created hundreds of jobs by starting businesses that mine the town's industries for reusable materials.

The Organization

Community of Arcata

The Opportunity

To create and retain jobs in a region that for more than a century had relied on timber and other extractive industries.

The Challenge

Creating profitable businesses that utilize the manpower and skills of the existing regional workforce.

The Solution

Promote a focus on sustainable development and the need to create businesses built around recycling and recycled products.

Arcata, in California's far north, has created economic stability through a broad-based effort to diversify and capitalize on the region's environmental consciousness. The loose network of environmental companies created in Arcata in recent years results not from a single government, private-sector, or nonprofit organization's efforts so much as a series of independent and collaborative efforts, according to Barbara O'Neal, executive director of the Center for Environmental Economic Development (CEED), a research and planning organization.

One example is Cascade Forest Products, which makes composts and mulches at a very low cost by obtaining 100,000 cubic yards of discarded wood materials a year from local sawmills. It employs 35 people and in 1994 had sales of $3.3 million. Another is

Fire and Light Originals, which has cultivated a direct link with the city's recycling system to market decorative glass tiles made with 100% post-consumer glass. Kokotat, a watersport clothing manufacturer, uses polyester made from recycled PET plastic; its material scraps, in turn, go to a stuffed animal maker. Another firm, Willow, makes a clothing line using Ecospun, a material comprised of reclaimed cotton and PET plastic.

Other environmental businesses are on the drawing board, including a doormat company that will use old tires, a rug company that will use scraps from local clothing manufacturers, and a company that would produce road construction materials using recycled concrete, asphalt, and rubber.

These and other businesses have had help from a number of sources, including CEED, the Arcata Community Recycling Center, the Arcata Economic Development Corporation (AEDC), and the state government, which designated Humbolt County a Recycling Market Development Zone in 1993. A Sustainable Development Loan Fund was created by AEDC in 1994 to support environmentally minded businesses.

The Bottom Line

Timber remains a mainstay of Humboldt County, but Arcata now has a light manufacturing base that many surrounding communities lack, making it better able to weather tough economic times. One encouraging sign is the county's unemployment figures: for 20 years, Humboldt County's unemployment was above the state's average. In 1994, that situation reversed.

For More Information

Center for Environmental Economic Development
1630 27th St.
Arcata, CA 95521
707-822-8347
707-822-4457 (fax)

Tread Setters

How do two entrepreneurs with a good idea but no real track record start a company that recycles old tires into innovative playground toys? With hard work, creativity—and a little help from the city, county, and state.

The Company

Create-A-Saurus

The Opportunity

To give hard-to-recycle truck tires a second life as innovative children's climbing structures for parks and playgrounds.

The Challenge

To provide business and financial assistance to a small startup company.

The Solution

Tap into state and local programs that provide assistance to job-creating environmental businesses.

Rudolph Peters, an educator, and Leanell Jones, a home builder and remodeler, had an idea: to create climbable dinosaur-like structures out of used truck tires. The dinosaurs—in three models, ranging from four feet high and 800 pounds to six feet high and 4,000 pounds—are ideal for parks, playgrounds, child-care centers, and other play areas. They are versatile, maintenance-free, and virtually indestructible. In addition to their environmental benefits, the structures comply with laws of accessibility for the physically disabled.

But Peters and Jones needed help turning their idea into a business, dubbed Create-A-Saurus by Jones's 10-year-old daughter. They turned to Oakland's Office of Economic Development and Employment, which administers the state's Oakland-Berkeley Recycling Market Development Zone, or RMDZ, one of 29 RMDZs throughout the state. The RMDZ helped Create-A-Saurus in several ways. It helped it win a $60,000 grant from the Alameda County Recycling Board's Waste Management Authority to purchase equipment and cover startup business costs. It also helped the new company join the Small Business Growth Center, a business incubator sponsored by the city of Oakland to provide technical assistance and low-cost office and warehouse space to new businesses. The incubator also provides clerical, phone, and mail services.

With this help, Peters and Jones were able to get their first order: construction and installation of four dinosaurs for the Oakland Parks and Recreation Department.

In its first year, Create-A-Saurus expanded into a second product line, making rubber surfacing for parks, hotels, locker rooms, swimming rooms, and decks. The rubber comes from the scrap created by tire retreaders, which otherwise would end up in landfills. Jones says his company will use more than 100,000 tons of shredded rubber a year.

The Bottom Line

Create-A-Saurus grew to 10 employees by the end of 1994, its first year of operation, and expected to add 15 more during 1995. The employees' pay ranges from $8 an hour to as high as $30 an hour for several highly skilled, customized-building jobs.

For More Information

Create-A-Saurus
P.O. Box 20031
Oakland, CA 94620
510-444-4520, ext. 12
510-633-1776 (fax)

Small Is Bountiful

Between 1989 and 1991, the nation's biggest job growth came from firms with fewer than 5 employees, says the U.S. Small Business Administration. But the success rate of small startups is historically low. What's the best way to turn small, environmental companies into job machines? A Silicon Valley organization may have the answer.

The Organization

Environmental Business Cluster

The Opportunity

To create a support system in which fledgling environmental businesses can grow, prosper, and create jobs.

The Challenge

Overcoming the risks and barriers faced by young companies during the treacherous early years, as well as providing continued guidance as companies grow.

The Solution

Create an incubator to "hatch" new companies.

Business incubators provide a relatively safe, protected environment in which entrepreneurs can start and build companies. The idea isn't new, but this is the first to focus on environmental businesses.

The Environmental Business Cluster, which opened in 1994, is the idea of Jim Robbins, who launched a high-tech cluster at Digital Equipment Corp. Robbins teamed up with several business groups as well as a local defense contractor, United Defense, which donated space to house 30 businesses. Funding came from a public-private partnership including Bank of America, Pacific Gas & Electric, the city of San Jose, the Peninsula Conservation Center, and Joint Venture: Silicon Valley.

The incubator's first tenants span a range of businesses, among them A&A Rock Science, providing equipment and related services for excavating contaminated soils; EnviroSoft, creating software to analyze products' recyclability and disassembly; EOSystems, commercializing a process to destroy hazardous waste; Green Earth Office Supply; Natural Literacy, a retailer of environmental books, maps, and software; Solarwatt, marketing a technology that converts sunlight into electricity; and Universal Solar Energy Applications, exporting solar technologies to developing countries.

Once accepted, cluster companies get below-market office space, access to research facilities, shared conference rooms, management assistance, marketing advice, financing assistance, and other services. Equally important is the cross-fertilization and information sharing that takes place simply from having several like-minded companies in the same building.

The Bottom Line

When filled to capacity, 100 people are expected to be employed in the cluster. But the real job-generating potential won't be known for years. "Nationally, the failure rate for startups is high, and environmental startups are probably worse," says Robbins, adding that 80% of businesses fail within the first three years. "Our goal is to turn that statistic on its head and have an 80% success rate."

Robbins is consulting to others interested in starting environmental business clusters. Already, clusters are slated to open in Thousand Oaks, north of Los Angeles, and in Chula Vista, near San Diego. The Chula Vista cluster is part of a larger, NAFTA-related environmental effort, aimed at enhancing trade of environmental products and services between Mexico and the U.S.

For More Information

Environmental Business Cluster
1830 Bering Dr., Ste. 3
San Jose, CA 95112
408-437-5678
408-437-5670 (fax)

Oil's Well

By developing a technology to turn used motor oil back into new motor oil, a California company has effectively created a new kind of oil well: one that pumps millions of gallons a year—not from beneath the ground or the oceans, but from service stations, lube centers, and repair shops.

The Company

Evergreen Oil

The Opportunity

To make a profit collecting hazardous waste oil and turning it into re-refined motor oil.

The Challenge

Developing a new technology and fostering customer acceptance for a new type of product.

The Solution

Create a closed-loop oil-recycling system.

Traditionally, used motor oil collected by service stations and others ended up as boiler fuel, often releasing hazardous pollutants into the air as it was burned. In 1984, Evergreen developed a technology to turn used oil back into re-refined oil, reducing the need for new oil as well as the disposal of polluted oil.

Evergreen's technology combines standard oil refining operations with a proprietary catalyst technology that yields about three quarts of new oil for every gallon recycled. The remaining quart ends up as water, which is treated and put into the sewer system, as well as diesel and gasoline, which are used to fire the company's heating system.

Today, Evergreen is the largest waste-oil collection and re-refining operation in California. It boasts a fleet of 53 trucks that in 1994 collected 18 million gallons of used oil and antifreeze from 15,000 service stations and lube-center operators in five states. Customers include Chevron, Unocal, Jiffy Lube, and Pennzoil lube centers. The company also was chosen to be the sole collector for the San Francisco showpiece oil-collection facility.

In addition to collecting used oil and antifreeze, a fleet of 15 Evergreen trucks collect contaminated waste water and provide emergency cleanup services for oil spills. In 1994, Evergreen's trucks collected 3.5 million gallons of waste water from more than 5,000 industrial customers.

Evergreen also services corporate customers, such as Pacific Bell, Pacific Gas & Electric, Southern California Edison, and the U.S. Postal Service, collecting used oil, oil filters, and antifreeze from fleet vehicles and replenishing the oils with Evergreen's re-refined products.

The Bottom Line

Evergreen Oil now employs 175 people, and expects to continue to grow. The potential for oil recycling is enormous: about 120 million gallons of motor oil are sold annually in California alone and about 95% of it is collectible.

For More Information

Evergreen Oil
5000 Birch St., Ste. 500
Newport Beach, CA 92660
714-757-7770
714-474-9149 (fax)

Package Deal

Polystyrene is not a toxic material, but it is bulky, lightweight, and expensive to transport. A Bay Area company has pioneered a process to recycle this ubiquitous material into a new packaging product.

The Company

Free-Flow Packaging Corp.

The Opportunity

To design and manufacture a means for recycling polystyrene products.

The Challenge

Create an economically viable system for collecting and recycling a bulky, lightweight material.

The Solution

Design a way to turn discarded polystyrene into a new packaging product.

Free-Flow's founder, Arthur Graham, is credited with launching the loosefill packaging industry in the 1950s, when he headed a company that made ice cream cones and paper soda straws. He used the ends snipped off straws as packaging, later using expanded polystyrene instead of paper to make loosefill. In the 1970s, he developed a process to make loosefill—what some people refer to as "packing peanuts"—from waste purchased from polystyrene manufacturers, rather than use virgin materials.

Today, Free-Flow has expanded its recycling operations. It accepts used foam polystyrene packaging from equipment manufacturers, such as Saturn Motors, Hewlett-Packard, and Apple Computer; from companies that have "take-back" programs for their products' packaging, such as Xerox and Canon; and from distribution centers, office parks, shopping malls, and individual businesses. In addition, the company has established several community recycling programs for polystyrene. In 1993, Free-Flow recycled 6.5 million pounds of polystyrene packaging, more than 20% of all polystyrene recycled in the U.S.

The company uses all the polystyrene it recycles to make Flo-Pak, a 100% waste-polystyrene loosefill, at six facilities in California, Delaware, Georgia, Illinois, and Massachusetts. It first grinds polystyrene into small pieces of fluff, which then is extruded into pellets. Various pellets are mixed, then extruded in long strands, shaped into figure-eights, cut, and expanded into finished loosefill.

The Bottom Line

Free-Flow Packaging has 300 employees in the U.S. and three European facilities. Since 1988, the company has hired approximately 30 new full-time workers at its U.S. plants for its recycling operations. Its sales in 1993 were $35 million.

For More Information

Free-Flow Packaging Corp.
1093 Charter St.
Redwood City, CA 94063
800-866-9946
415-364-1145
415-361-1713 (fax)

Profits From Thin Air

California is the world's biggest backer of alternative energy sources. The state boasts 50% of the world's geothermal power plants, 82% of the installed wind-energy capacity, and 99% of utility-scale solar generation. Wind power is a key part of the mix, and one company leads the way.

The Company

Kenetech Windpower

The Opportunity

To make wind-generated electricity a viable source of the state's energy grid.

The Challenge

Creating a new generation of utility-grade wind turbines that compete in cost-efficiency with traditional energy sources.

The Solution

Form partnerships with utility companies to ensure wind power competes effectively with traditional electricity-generating fuels and technologies.

Although Kenetech has successfully demonstrated the potential of wind power since 1979 (when it was originally incorporated as U.S. Windpower), the technology was not cost-effective for large utilities. A consortium involving Kenetech, Pacific Gas & Electric, Niagara-Mohawk Power Corp. (a New York utility), the Electric Power Research Institute, and others created the funding to develop efficient, large-scale turbines.

Kenetech's turbines are a far cry from the clumsy, metal windmills seen on so many farms. Today's wind energy comes from 140-foot towers with 80-foot-diameter blades on a "wind farm." The power is distributed over transmission lines to major metropolitan areas. The new technology has helped Kenetech grow into the world's biggest wind turbine manufacturer. The company owns half the 7,000 turbines that dot the 80-square-mile Altamont Pass wind farm east of San Francisco and sells power to Pacific Gas & Electric, San Diego Gas & Electric Co., and other utilities.

Increasingly, some of the company's biggest customers are abroad. For example, Kenetech signed an agreement in 1993 to supply 5,000 windmills to the Ukraine to help the country end its energy reliance on the Chernobyl nuclear plant. The windmills will produce enough electricity to serve 400,000 Ukrainian households. In 1994, the company announced plans to build a wind-power plant in Costa Rica to provide nearly 3% of the country's energy needs.

The Bottom Line

Kenetech has grown from just over 600 employees in 1992 to roughly 1,200 employees; it expects to double employment by 1996. The benefits of Kenetech's turbines extend beyond its own employees. The installations provide local construction jobs and generate royalties for landowners who allow turbines on their property. In most cases, the leased land is still viable for agriculture, grazing, and other uses.

Wind power currently provides less than 1% of total energy generating capacity in the U.S. According to the Department of Energy, wind could contribute as much as 20% within a decade. Ironically, California is not a very windy state. One study ranked the state 29th among the lower 48 in wind energy potential. In contrast, the wind resources of Kansas, North Dakota, South Dakota, and Texas, if completely developed, could provide more than half the nation's electricity needs.

For More Information

Kenetech Windpower
6952 Preston Ave.
Livermore, CA 94550
415-398-3825
415-391-7740 (fax)

Cleanup Batters

According to the Environmental Business International, U.S. companies spent $8.9 billion in 1994 to clean up existing environmental problems, such as hazardous waste dumps, some of them decades old. Helping companies comply with regulations in cost-efficient ways has created a boom industry for consultants, environmental engineers, and others.

The Company

McLaren Hart

The Opportunity

To help companies comply with increasingly stringent environmental, health, and safety laws.

The Challenge

To limit companies' present and future liabilities, while identifying opportunities for going beyond regulatory compliance to improve bottom-line performance.

The Solution

Provide a range of services to help companies stay in compliance—and stay profitable.

Twenty-five years ago, complying with environmental laws meant operating with good intentions. But thousands of companies found themselves burdened years later with high cleanup costs, despite the fact they were operating in full compliance with then-current laws. Today, companies face much more stringent inspections and accountability than ever before.

McLaren Hart, established in 1977, aims to help companies get out of environmental trouble, or avoid it in the first place. At the core of its services are audits. Six different formalized audits and assessments not only ensure that environmental safety is part of management's agenda, but also promote a philosophy of compliance within the company's management structure. For example, management system audits qualitatively evaluate a company's operating and administrative systems aimed at controlling environmental and safety matters. Compliance audits scrutinize operations to identify where they are not in full compliance with federal, state, or local regulations. Waste minimization audits identify opportunities to reduce solid waste by recycling, process redesign, or other means. The company also assists with hazardous waste cleanup, including designing and building cleanup systems.

"There's always going to be a need for compliance," says McLaren Hart vice president David Nunenkamp. "Those of us who work in California really feel that the regulations need to be updated about once every hour. That's how frequently they change. Preservation of the environment is clearly paramount for us all, but most companies cannot afford to have a number of individuals engaged in compliance full time. So I think the demand for consulting services is going to be there for a long time."

The Bottom Line

McLaren Hart employs nearly 700 people in 16 offices nationwide and four international offices. An estimated 110 jobs have been created in the past two years. The need for the kind of services offered by McLaren Hart continues to grow. According to Environmental Business International, a San Diego research and publishing firm, the projected market for environmental consulting, engineering, and remediation services within California will grow to more than $3.7 billion by 1998, employing more than 39,000 people.

For More Information

McLaren Hart
11101 White Rock Rd.
Rancho Cordova, CA 95670
916-638-3696
916-638-3690 (fax)

Where Credit Is Due

While California boasts hundreds of small environmental businesses, many of them need financial assistance to grow into larger, job-creating companies. But finding funding for small firms with unproven track records can be tough. A state program that offers low-interest loans is designed to help.

The Company

The Plactory

The Opportunity

To create profitable local manufacturing operations using recycled plastics as a raw material.

The Challenge

Finding affordable financing to establish or expand job-producing environmental technologies.

The Solution

A low-interest loan provided by the State of California.

The Plactory, based in Santa Cruz, is located in the Central Coast Recycling Market Development Zone (RMDZ). One key component is a financing program that provides direct loans to recycling businesses and local governments located in RMDZs. Funds may be used for property, equipment, working capital, or refinancing current debt. Priority is given to projects showing potential to significantly increase market demand for that material type, leverage other private capital, and that manufacture recycled-content products or use innovative technologies. Eligible businesses may borrow up to 50% of the cost of the project, up to $1 million.

The Central Coast RMDZ is offering businesses financial incentives to develop ways of reusing locally discarded materials currently being shipped to Oakland and Los Angeles. Local landfills are taxed. Almost 2 million cubic yards of waste are sent to the area landfills each year, say Watsonville officials, who estimate that dumps will be full within eight years.

The Plactory borrowed $75,000 through the RMDZ program, and was required to invest a matching sum. The loan was used to buy a "pelletizer/extruder" that would allow the company to work with recycled plastics, such as PET and HDPE, commonly used for soda bottles and milk jugs. The company uses the pelletizer to regrind recycled plastic, which is turned into new plastic display racks and other items for retail use.

The Bottom Line

The company now has 15 employees and $1 million in annual sales. The RMDZ loan "worked out pretty well," says company president Steven Suess. "When word got out that we were using recycled plastics, others came down to see what revolutionary technology we were using. The fact is, we were just using old equipment, but had learned how to work with recycled materials." In 1994, the company was honored by the California Resource Recovery Association for its work with recycled materials.

The California Integrated Waste Management Board estimates that through RMDZs, 20,000 jobs could be created in manufacturing, along with another 25,000 in sorting and processing recyclables, and thousands more in multiplier effects.

For More Information

The Plactory
986 Tower Pl.
Santa Cruz, CA 95062
408-462-1565
408-462-4368 (fax)

Breaking Down Is Hard to Do

For years, the quest for environmentally friendly plastics has been fierce, but results were elusive. So-called "degradable" plastics did not break down easily, or they degraded into harmful substances. But a San Diego company has created a line of plastic resins and is poised to tap a huge market.

The Company

Planet Polymer Technologies, Inc.

The Opportunity

To produce plastics that easily degrade into harmless materials when disposed of or composted.

The Challenge

Many previous efforts to produce degradable plastics proved ineffective or not cost-competitive with virgin plastics.

The Solution

EnviroPlastic, a unique plastic resin that degrades into harmless material in water or when composted, and which can match the physical properties of many conventional plastics.

The material was created by Dr. Robert Petcavich, inspired after encountering the plastic trash on a San Diego beach. EnviroPlastic resins come in several versions, each with its own properties. For example, some of the water-soluble plastics degrade in a few seconds of contact with water, while others take several weeks to dissolve. Some resins are designed for molding, others for hot-melt processes. Suitable uses, says the company, range from pesticide packaging to six-pack rings, paper coatings to feminine hygiene products. The resins can be used with most existing manufacturing machinery.

One promising product is a degradable plastic coating for cardboard boxes that dissolves during repulping (recycling) operations.

That will permit even more cardboard to be recycled rather than landfilled. "The big mistake other degradable plastics manufacturers made was trying to create their own infrastructure," says Petcavich. "We've designed our products to be compatible with existing equipment."

Price is the remaining challenge. Current prices of EnviroPlastic remain 50% to 100% above virgin plastics. But Petcavich says he expects mass production of the materials to drive prices down to be competitive with virgin by 1996.

The Bottom Line

Some experts predict that degradables will command at least 5% of the plastics market within a few years, and as much as 50% to 60% of the market of some sectors, such as agriculture. So far, Planet Polymer Technologies has only 10 employees, but there is great potential. In 1994, the company licensed Korea Kumho Petrochemical exclusive marketing rights for EnviroPlastic in South Korea, and other deals are expected.

For More Information

Planet Polymer Technologies, Inc.
9985 Businesspark Ave., Ste. A
San Diego, CA 92131
619-549-5130
619-549-5133 (fax)

Fuel's Paradise

Compressed natural gas is a fuel with promise. It can power cars, trucks, and buses more safely, economically, and with fewer emissions than most other fuels. It is abundant, and because it comes from domestic sources, reduces the need to import foreign oil. As a state transit district found, it also can help drive jobs.

The Company

SunLine Transit Agency

The Opportunity

To create the first public transit system powered entirely by compressed natural gas (CNG), which is less polluting and more economical than gasoline, diesel, and methanol fuels.

The Challenge

To finance and create an infrastructure along with the technological expertise to enable a suburban bus company to fuel its buses with CNG, despite the widespread area served by the buses.

The Solution

Establish a partnership between SunLine and the local gas company, government agencies, and others.

In 1991, SunLine Transit, with 47 buses throughout the Coachella Valley (including Palm Springs, eight other municipalities, and portions of eastern Riverside County) had the second-oldest bus fleet in the country. Recognizing it had to replace its fleet, SunLine decided to buy 40 alternative-fuel vehicles—a $10 million project.

Cost wasn't the only factor. How would the company fuel its buses? Who would repair them? Answers came through a series of partnerships. Southern California Gas Company promised that if SunLine converted its entire fleet to CNG, it would build a 24-hour, public-access fueling station that would be the largest in southern California. SunLine then approached College of the Desert, the local community college, and asked what it could do to train mechanics. The result: the Energy Technology Training Center, the first U.S. training facility for maintaining alternative-fuel vehicles.

Financing for the bus purchases came from a variety of sources: federal grants and loan guarantees, Riverside County funds, state transportation assistance funds, and the South Coast Air Quality Management District. In addition to the buses, SunLine converted its fleet of cars and trucks to CNG.

"Building partnerships builds community excitement, and builds acceptance for a new fuel," says Tracy A. Daly, SunLine's director of resource development. "Our partnerships are welcome in our community because they are achieving great things for the Coachella Valley."

The Bottom Line

SunLine's switch to CNG has created at least 28 jobs, and has saved the company on fuel costs. Through an arrangement with Southern California Gas, SunLine will earn a credit of seven cents for each therm of CNG sold from its station. Because fuel is SunLine's second-highest cost, this has motivated the company to market its refueling services to other CNG users.

Experts predict that at least 180,000 natural gas vehicles will be in use by the year 2000 in southern California, supported by 600 refueling stations at public and private locations. Converting, fueling, and maintaining these vehicles is expected to create more than 7,000 new jobs.

For More Information

SunLine Transit Agency
32-505 Harry Oliver Trail
Thousand Palms, CA 92276
619-343-3456
619-343-3845 (fax)

Taking the Wrap

Making plastic recycling cost-effective has been one of the biggest recycling challenges for most communities. In southern California, one company is proving that being a national leader in plastic recycling can be profitable.

The Company

Talco Plastics, Inc.

The Opportunity

To create new products and markets using recycled bottles and other plastic goods collected from recycling programs.

The Challenge

Making recycled plastic products cost-competitive with those made from virgin materials.

The Solution

Develop technology and expertise to recycle dozens of hard-to-recycle products to become a versatile "supermarket" of plastic recycling.

Talco Plastics began business in 1972 as a brokerage for the sale of scrap plastic, later adding a recycling operation for scrap plastic from manufacturers. Since then, the company has established one of the most comprehensive recycling operations, collecting and recycling more than 50 different types of plastic. Talco maintains an inventory of more than 10 million pounds of recycled plastics.

In 1990, the company began collecting postconsumer plastic from community recycling programs. In 1994, with the help of a loan from the California Integrated Waste Management Board, it constructed a plant in Long Beach exclusively to handle postconsumer plastic, including such difficult-to-recycle resins as polypropylene, polycarbonates, polyvinyl chloride, and ABS. Within six months of operation, the Long Beach plant reached its maximum handling capacity of 10 million tons a year, says Talco president John Shedd. He expects to eventually triple the plant's capacity.

Talco continues to expand the products it can handle. In 1994, the company began recycling such durable products as computer housings and appliances, as well as plastic grocery bags, stretch wraps, agricultural films, nylon, and acrylic.

The Bottom Line

Talco Plastics, with 175 employees, has become one of the top-10 recyclers of postconsumer plastics in the United States, according to industry statistics. While the company has been profitable ever since Shedd purchased it in 1988, he says profits have risen sharply due to California laws, mandating that many rigid containers and trash bags sold in the state contain postconsumer recycled material. "The mandatory legislation is the reason that I went into the postconsumer recycling business," says Shedd. "It's also the reason we're growing."

For More Information

Talco Plastics, Inc.
11650 Burke St.
Whittier, CA 90606
310-699-0550
310-692-6008 (fax)

Testing Their Metal

Steel is the single-most-recycled material in the United States. But some steel is contaminated—with motor oil, chemicals, and other toxic ingredients. Keeping that material out of landfills in a safe and cost-efficient manner has become a profitable endeavor for one California steel mill.

The Company

TAMCO

The Opportunity

To manufacture steel from recycled ferrous scrap metal, including from metal contaminated with hazardous materials, which had previously been unrecyclable.

The Challenge

Working with regulators to remove barriers to recycling some steel products.

The Solution

A new system to efficiently process used oil filters, producing an inexpensive source of raw material.

TAMCO is a steel mill whose primary raw material is millions of tons a year of waste ferrous scrap metal—material which otherwise would be deposited in a landfill. From that scrap it produces steel reinforcing bar for the construction industry. At TAMCO's San Bernardino County mini-mill—California's only steel mill—scrap metal is melted into molten scrap, analyzed, tested, and then formed, cooled, and solidified. The strands of solidified steel are formed into reinforcing bars and cut to various lengths. It takes TAMCO about three to four hours to turn scrap metal into a new product.

Not all the scrap TAMCO receives can be turned into steel. Some of it—about 2%—is hazardous waste, which must be carefully and safely collected. Until a few years ago, the dusty material was shipped to hazardous-waste landfills. Now it is being recycled at special facilities in Tennessee, Illinois, and Pennsylvania. The recycling not only limits liabilities, but also cuts dust management costs by half.

In 1991, TAMCO was challenged by the California Environmental Protection Agency to find a means of recycling used oil filters, which are made primarily of steel. Working with various state and local agencies, TAMCO developed a process to collect and recycle the used oil contained in the filters, decontaminate the metal, crush the filters, and turn them into new steel products. The process yields millions of gallons of oil, metal—and no hazardous or solid waste. The program is now being expanded nationally. "It was one of those examples where government basically stepped back and let industry take the lead in resolving the challenge," says TAMCO's environmental manager, Leonard Robinson.

The Bottom Line

Since 1991, TAMCO has recycled over 20 million used oil filters, roughly 10,000 tons' worth, yielding at least 17 million pounds of recovered steel, recycling 31,000 gallons of oil that would have leaked into landfills, and saving 100,000 cubic yards of landfill space. The company has 350 employees, who earn $12 to $15 an hour, plus benefits. It also has a low annual turnover rate of 6%.

TAMCO's oil filter recycling operation has had other job-creating benefits. The company says that approximately 50 new businesses or divisions within existing businesses have been formed to support used oil filter recycling.

For More Information

TAMCO
P.O. Box 325
Rancho Cucamonga, CA 91739
909-899-0660
909-899-1910 (fax)

A Driving Force

By 1998, auto makers must offer for sale in California 30,000 to 40,000 new cars and light trucks that will not pollute the air. Other states have similar mandates. That points to electric vehicles. Meeting those goals will require a new generation of car makers. One fast-growing company has paved the way.

The Company

U.S. Electricar, Inc.

The Opportunity

To become a leading independent producer of electric-powered cars and light trucks for company fleets.

The Challenge

Creating technological breakthroughs and manufacturing capacity in a small company, while remaining competitive against larger ventures.

The Solution

Establish a niche business not covered by the "Big Three" auto makers.

U.S. Electricar targets operators of large fleets and then converts their vehicles to electric engines. Over the past decade, the company has emerged as the nation's leader in converting cars and trucks from conventional gasoline to electric power. Without the help of any major manufacturer and with its own money, the company says it has proven that electric vehicles are viable.

The company has grown significantly, thanks to a combination of increased sales as well as mergers and acquisitions of other electric car and component makers. Also leading to its growth are partnerships. For example, in 1994, U.S. Electricar and Itochu Corp., one of the world's largest trading companies, formed a joint venture to target Tokyo's market for light delivery trucks. U.S. Electricar is also designing an electric vehicle from the ground up that it hopes to eventually sell in Japan.

Another joint venture is with Niagara-Mohawk Power Corp., an upstate New York utility. Niagara-Mohawk formed a partnership with U.S. Electricar to produce, maintain, and market electric vehicles. The partnership plans to build a production facility in central New York in 1995.

The Bottom Line

The company, which recorded $2 million in sales in 1993, had revenues of $15 million in 1994. In 1995, predicts company vice president Carl Perry, the company will produce 3,500 electric vehicles—more than any of the Big Three auto makers. During an 18-month period in 1993-1994, U.S. Electricar's work force grew from 30 to 400 employees through acquisitions and expansion. Many of these are skilled jobs paying $7 to $14 an hour. Moreover, when U.S. Electricar opened a plant in Carson in 1994, it targeted an area near riot-torn South-Central Los Angeles. The plant employs 100 employees, most of whom are minorities.

Researchers at UCLA predict that building electric cars will generate at least 24,000 jobs in southern California by 2003. Other estimates range as high as 55,000 new jobs by the end of the decade. Most jobs won't be in final assembly, say the experts, but in production and sub-assembly of such electric vehicle parts as motors, controllers, transmissions, frames, body panels, doors, and seats.

For More Information

U.S. Electricar, Inc.
P.O. Box 6645
Santa Rosa, CA 95406
707-525-3227
707-525-3224 (fax)

Mining the Metropolis

What do you do with a broken kitchen sink? What about old furniture and appliances? In the past, there was no choice but to send it to a landfill. But a Richmond company has shown there's still potential—and profit—in these treasures.

The Company

Urban Ore

The Opportunity

To create and manage a business network of recycling and reuse facilities for a wide range of discarded goods and materials.

The Challenge

Creating a profitable system to collect, sort, refurbish, and resell or distribute materials for which cost-effective recycling doesn't always exist.

The Solution

Link with other businesses and nonprofit organizations to form a "serial materials recovery facility," or serial MRF.

Since 1980, Urban Ore has made a successful business collecting and reselling a variety of discarded materials that still had a useful life: furniture, rugs, housewares, books, office equipment, and other goods. The company also runs a building materials exchange for doors, windows, sinks, tubs, toilets, lumber, bricks, glass, tile, pipe, and other remnants of buildings and construction.

In 1992, Urban Ore formed a loose coalition with other recycling businesses, nonprofit organizations, and the city of Berkeley to create a network of disposal opportunities for unwanted materials. Now, materials collected at curbside or brought into recycling centers can be taken to any of several organizations that collect and resell them. Urban Ore and others accept these materials, usually at no charge, that might otherwise have cost their owners in transportation and disposal fees. Each organization in the network accepts different types of materials.

"Basically, we're a bunch of niche recyclers who are all practicing in the same locality," says Daniel Knapp, Urban Ore president and co-founder. "The fact is this works on a societal level. It works really, really well.

"Anyone can do this," continues Knapp. "Entrepreneurial behavior is not really limited to businesses. Nonprofit organizations, governments, anyone can act entrepreneurally."

The Bottom Line

Urban Ore, with annual revenue of about $1.5 million, has 18 full-time and 10 part-time employees, who earn $9.50 to $18.50 an hour, based on a bonus system tied to sales and tonnage, plus additional benefits. The company has practically no turnover. In addition, the other five companies, agencies, and organizations participating in the coalition employ approximately 70 people. All of these organizations also use independent contractors for everything from brick cleaning to trucking.

For More Information

Urban Ore, Inc.
6082 Ralston Ave.
Richmond, CA 94805
510-235-0172
510-235-0198 (fax)

Clearing the Air

With a little ingenuity, some determination, and some help from a local utility company, one company found that complying with tough environmental regulations not only created jobs, it also created profits.

The Company

West Coast Samples

The Opportunity

To change manufacturing processes to produce a product with fewer emissions and a lower cost.

The Challenge

Complying with increasingly stringent air-quality regulations without downsizing, leaving the state, or going out of business.

The Solution

A partnership with the local electric utility to create a printing process that eliminates emissions of nearly all air pollutants.

West Coast Samples, a manufacturer of swatch and sample books—distributed to paint, wallpaper, home-decorating, and interior design stores—faced a tough new mandate to reduce or eliminate smog-producing volatile organic compounds (VOCs) from its printing operation. The company had been using a traditional silk-screen process to imprint covers, binders, and rigid papers, a process that emitted VOCs.

Working with Southern California Edison's Clean Air Coatings Technologies Program, West Coast Samples learned about an ultraviolet (UV) technology that could replace the conventional system, eliminating VOC-producing inks and heat dryers.

The company already had been planning to move its facility to Chino, because it had outgrown its existing capacity in La Puente. The new plant included the installation of UV printing process as well as other energy-saving technologies: motion sensors to turn off lights in empty rooms, timers to turn equipment on and off as needed, and a system to separate toxic chemicals from waste water.

The Bottom Line

West Coast Samples brought 90 employees to its new headquarters in Chino. Within a year of the move and installation of the new UV system, the payroll grew to 220 employees, with more hiring planned. One reason: Switching to UV allowed the company to more than double its production speeds. Profits are up, too—more than 25% in just one year, due in part to the UV system's cost savings. For example, where conventional inks cost $50 a gallon and produce 1,000 printed units, UV inks cost $100 a gallon yet produce 4,000 units. The UV inks are safer for workers, too.

Southern California's other major sample-book manufacturers, finding themselves facing similar challenges, took very different courses. One downsized, one moved to another state, and another moved to Mexico. A fourth shut down operation altogether.

Says company president Larry Barrios: "When we moved to Chino, we felt proud that we could keep employees together with their families and keep our industry in California while utilizing new technologies and reducing air pollution."

For More Information

West Coast Samples
14450 Central Ave.
Chino, CA 91710
909-464-1616
909-465-9982 (fax)

PART THREE

Resources

Resources

The listings below include regulatory, technological, informational, and financial assistance for California businesses seeking to link environmental success with financial success. The resources include state and local government agencies, federal government agencies, and nonprofit groups.

You are encouraged to contact these organizations to seek help with such matters as:

- understanding and complying with federal, state, or local environmental laws;
- going beyond compliance to reduce wastes and emissions, or improve energy efficiency;
- starting or expanding a business that offers environmental products or services;
- seeking recycled or environmentally improved products to purchase, or markets to sell your company's recycled or environmentally improved products; and
- financial assistance for making environmental improvements.

State Government Offices

Resources Agency

• Department of Conservation

Publishes *California Market Watch*, a free database, updated monthly, that lists recycled-content products and manufacturers, dealers, processors, and equipment suppliers. Publishes *California Recycling Review*, a free technical bulletin published 10 times a year to disseminate recycling information. Administers InfoCycle, an electronic bulletin board developed as a forum for individuals and organizations to access recycling information. (Call 916-445-1490 for general information, or 916-445-0518 to access InfoCycle directly.) Sponsors a comprehensive buy-recycled public-information campaign. (Call 800-RECYCLE for more information.)

Department of Conservation
Division of Recycling
801 K St.
Sacramento, CA 95814
916-323-3508
800-RECYCLE (Toll-free Information)
916-324-1224 (fax)

Environmental Protection Agency

Offers California Environmental Technology Partnership, representing government, industry, financial institutions, academia, and public interest groups to promote and assist the development, manufacture, use, and export of California-based environmental technologies, goods, and services. Features a data base and information clearinghouse. Offers hazardous waste reduction grants to promote the development of innovative hazardous waste reduction, recycling, or treatment projects and technologies.

Environmental Protection Agency
555 Capitol Mall, Ste. 235
Sacramento, CA 95814
800-808-8058 (Help Desk)
916-322-2822 (Calif. Environmental Technology Partnership)
916-322-7287 (Hazardous Waste Reduction Grant Program)
916-323-1923 (fax)

- **Air Resources Board**

Small Business Assistance Program helps companies comply with emissions standards for cars, trucks, and buses in order to obtain operating permits.

Air Resources Board
Stationary Source Division
P.O. Box 2815
Sacramento, CA 95812
916-322-8273 (General Information)
916-323-4883 (Small Business Assistance Program)
916-445-5023 (fax)

• Integrated Waste Management Board
Administers the Recycling Market Development Zone program, providing economic development, technical expertise, and low-interest loans to spur recycling. Also administers the California Materials Exchange, or CALMAX, a waste exchange to help businesses find users for materials that are traditionally discarded.

Integrated Waste Management Board
8800 Cal Center Dr.
Sacramento, CA 95826
800-553-2962 (Recycling Hotline)
916-255-2289 (General Public Information)

• Department of Toxic Substances Control
Provides management consultations to help reduce liabilities in the storage, transport, and treatment of toxic waste. Aims to ease regulatory burdens of small businesses.

Department of Toxic Substances Control
Office of Pollution Prevention and Technology Development
P.O. Box 806
Sacramento, CA 95812
916-322-3670
916-327-4494 (fax)

• Water Resources Control Board
Administers the Underground Storage Tank and Stormwater programs. Holds regional roundtables to share information with businesses seeking to reduce waste at the source. There are regional boards located in the state's nine major watersheds. They issue permits for those wishing to discharge into water bodies of the region.

Water Resources Control Board
Office of Legislative and Public Affairs
P.O. Box 100
Sacramento, CA 95812
916-657-1247
916-227-4303 (Underground Storage Tank Program)
916-657-0919 (Stormwater Program)
916-657-1812 (fax)

Trade and Commerce Agency, Office of Small Business

Operates 24 regional Small Business Development Centers that provide free services to small business owners. Also contracts with several Small Business Development Corporations, nonprofit regional organizations that administer a menu of federal and state loan and loan-guarantee programs for businesses. Offers small-business loans of up to $750,000 through California Loans for Environmental Assistance Now (CLEAN) Program. Other loan programs cover energy conservation and underground storage tank repair or removal. Also administers the California Enterprise Zone Program. Companies that locate or expand in a designated Enterprise Zone can take advantage of tax incentives and marketing assistance.

Trade and Commerce Agency
Office of Small Business
801 K St., Ste. 1700
Sacramento, CA 95814
916-324-5068 (General Information)
916-445-6733 (Loan Program Information)
916-327-HELP (Small Business Helpline)
916-322-5084 (fax)

Business, Transportation, and Housing Agency

Finances resources and provides advocacy, marketing, and technical assistance through the Trade and Commerce Agency. Its Hazardous Waste Reduction Loan program helps companies finance equipment purchases that can reduce waste generation or lessen the hazardous properties of waste.

Business, Transportation, and Housing Agency
Small Business Advocate
1120 N St., Rm. 2101
Sacramento, CA 95814
800-303-6600
916-327-HELP
916-324-1296 (fax)

– State Government Assistance Programs –

• Hazardous Waste Reduction Loan Program
Administers funds for local programs aimed at technologies and plans to reduce hazardous waste.

Department of Commerce
Office of Small Business
801 K St., Ste. 1700
Sacramento, CA 95814
916-323-9879
916-322-5084 (fax)

• Underground Storage Tank Loan Program
Administers loan program for owners of underground fuel-storage tanks to help with environmental regulatory compliance.

Underground Storage Tank Loan Program
801 K St., Ste. 1600
Sacramento, CA 95814
916-324-9325
916-322-5084 (fax)

• SCAQMD Small Business Assistance Office
Conducts no-fault air-quality inspections, identifies rules that apply to small businesses and helps them apply for air-control permits; also loans $50,000 to $250,000 to small businesses for air-control devices through the Air Quality Assistance Fund.

Small Business Assistance Office
South Coast Air Quality Management District
21865 E. Copley Dr.
Diamond Bar, CA 91765
800-388-2121
909-396-2372
909-396-3335 (fax)

• Local Government Commission
Serves local governments on a variety of topics. Services include Recyclink, an electronic bulletin board system accessible by personal computer that provides information on recycling programs.

Local Government Commission
1414 K St., Ste. 250
Sacramento, CA 95814
916-448-1198
916-448-8246 (fax)

• Pollution Control Financing Authority
Provides loans to small businesses for acquisition, construction, or installation of qualified pollution-control, waste-disposal, and resource-recovery facilities.

Pollution Control Financing Authority
915 Capitol Mall, Rm. 466
Sacramento, CA 95814
916-654-5610
916-657-4821 (fax)

• South Coast Air Quality Management District
Supports research, development, and demonstration of advanced emissions control technologies and clean fuels. This public-private partnership involves both mobile (especially electric buses and vehicles) and stationary sources of air pollution. Also provides financial assistance for small business for air pollution control equipment or dismantling of old equipment in order to start a different, more innovative project; and grants to local, state, federal, and nonprofit agencies for projects that reduce the environmental impact of transportation.

Technology Advancement Office
South Coast Air Quality Management District
21865 E. Copley Dr.
Diamond Bar, CA 91765
909-396-3250
909-396-3252 (fax)

Local Programs

North Coast Pollution Prevention Committee
Humboldt County Division of Environmental Health
100 H St., Ste. 100
Eureka, CA 95501
707-441-2003
707-441-5699 (fax)

Central Valley Hazardous Waste Minimization Committee
Water Quality Division
9660 Ecology Ln.
Sacramento, CA 95827
916-855-8354
916-855-5874 (fax)

San Joaquin County
Environmental Health Division
P.O. Box 388
Stockton, CA 95201
209-468-3451
209-464-0138 (fax)

Bay Area Hazardous Waste Reduction Committee
East Bay Municipal Utility Dist.
P.O. Box 24055
Oakland, CA 94623
510-287-1627
510-287-1530 (fax)

Marin County Office of Waste Management
10 N. San Pedro Rd., Ste. 1022
San Rafael, CA 94903
415-499-6647
415-499-6910 (fax)

EBMUD Source Control Div.
375 11th St. MS-702
Oakland, CA 94607
510-287-1511
510-287-1530 (fax)

City of Los Angeles
Integrated Solid Waste Management Office
200 N. Main St., Rm. 580
Los Angeles, CA 90012
213-237-1444
213-847-3054 (fax)

Los Angeles Hazardous Waste Reduction Assistance Prog.
Board of Public Works
200 N. Spring St., Rm. 353
Los Angeles, CA 90012
213-237-1209
213-237-1445 (fax)

Operation Clean Sweep
Board of Public Works
200 N. Spring St.
Los Angeles, CA 90012
213-485-6651
213-237-1445 (fax)

Southern California Pollution Prevention Committee
Orange County Environmental Health, Hazardous Materials Management
2009 E. Edinger Ave.
Santa Ana, CA 92705
714-667-3629
714-972-0749 (fax)

City of Placentia
Environmental Services
401 E. Chapman Ave.
Placentia, CA 92670
714-993-8117
714-961-0283 (fax)

City of San Diego
Environmental Services Dept.
202 C St.
San Diego, CA 92101
619-236-6844
619-236-6056 (fax)

Keep California Beautiful Affiliates

Each of these agencies and organizations offers environmental education and consulting for businesses, focusing on workplace recycling, source reduction, and other solid-waste management issues.

Downey Community Development Department
P.O. Box 7016
Downey, CA 90241
310-904-7159
310-904-7270 (fax)

Fresno County Clean Community Committee
2220 Tulare St., 6th Fl.
Fresno, CA 93721
209-453-5059
209-453-8566 (fax)

We Mean Clean Program
1 City Hall Plaza
Oakland, CA 94612
510-238-7630
510-238-7286 (fax)

Keep Riverside Clean
3685 Main St., Ste. 350
Riverside, CA 92501
909-683-7100
909-683-2670 (fax)

San Bernardino County
Environmental Health
22534 Pico St.
Grand Terrace, CA 92324
909-387-3177
909-387-4323 (fax)

I Love a Clean San Diego
7907 Ostrow St., Ste. F
San Diego, CA 92111
619-467-0103
619-467-1314 (fax)

San Jose Beautiful
333 W. Santa Clara, Ste. 800
San Jose, CA 95113
408-277-5208
408-277-3155 (fax)

Keep San Mateo Beautiful
City of San Mateo
1949 Pacific Blvd.
San Mateo, CA 95113
415-377-4630
415-377-4729 (fax)

Keep Santa Ana Beautiful
P.O. Box 1988 — M23
Santa Ana, CA 92702
714-647-6561
714-571-4235 (fax)

Seaside Neighborhood Improvement
440 Harcourt Ave.
Seaside, CA 93955
408-899-6209
408-899-6311 (fax)

Clean Tahoe
3368 Lake Tahoe Blvd., Ste. 208
So. Lake Tahoe, CA 96150
916-544-4210
916-544-5710 (fax)

Federal Assistance Programs

• **Advanced Technology Program**
Provides technology development funds to individual businesses and joint ventures to develop and accelerate the commercialization of high-risk technologies.

Advanced Technology Program
National Institute of Standards and Technology
Bldg. 101, Rm. 430
Gaithersburg, MD 20899
800-ATP-FUND (General Information)
301-975-4447
301-926-9524 (fax)

• **AgSTAR**
Promotes cost-effective methods for capturing methane releases from manure for use as on-farm energy. Participants commit to installing AgSTAR-selected technology wherever profitable.

AgSTAR Program Director
U.S. EPA (6202J)
401 M St. SW
Washington, DC 20460
202-233-9041
202-233-9569 (fax)

• **Agriculture in Concert with the Environment**
Helps farmers reduce pollution from pesticides and fertilizers.

Agriculture Coordinator
U.S. EPA (MC7409)
401 M St. SW, 7501W
Washington, DC 20460
703-308-8139
703-308-7026 (fax)

• **Business and Industrial Loan Guarantees**
Provides loan guarantees to companies in rural areas that develop or finance business or industry, increase employment, or control pollution.

Business and Industry Division
Rural Development Administration
USDA-RDA/B1
14th and Independence Ave. SW, Rm. 6321
Washington, DC 20250
202-690-4100
202-690-3808 (fax)

• **Design for the Environment**
Provides incentives for pollution prevention by helping companies incorporate environmental design into products. Helps businesses evaluate risks, performance, and cost of alternative, less-polluting chemicals. Awards grants to fund technology on a per-project basis.

Design for the Environment
Office of Pollution Prevention and Toxics
U.S. EPA
401 M St. SW
Washington, DC 20460
202-260-0667
202-260-0981 (fax)

• Energy Efficiency and Renewable Energy Clearinghouse
A service of the Department of Energy to provide technical assistance to businesses and others on alternative fuels, photovoltaics, wind energy, solar heating and cooling, buildings, and weatherization. Helps businesses with planning and development, locates sources of capital and financing, identifies viable markets and probable competition, and assesses possible legal and regulatory hurdles. Accessible through toll-free hotline, computer bulletin board, fax, and Internet e-mail.

Energy Efficiency and Renewable Energy Clearinghouse
P.O. Box 3048
Merrifield, VA 22116
800-363-3732
800-273-2957 (TDD)
800-273-2955 (BBS)
703-893-0400 (fax)

• Energy-Related Inventions Program
Offers free technical evaluation, market assessment, grants, and other assistance for inventions that save or produce energy. Any new energy-related concept, device, product, material, or industrial process with commercial potential may qualify.

Office of Technology Evaluation and Assessment
National Institute of Standards and Technology
Bldg. 411, Rm. A115
Gaithersburg, MD 20899
301-975-5500
301-975-3839 (fax)

• Energy Star Buildings
Helps building owners and managers improve the energy efficiency of their facilities. Participants receive technical information to optimize the performance of heating, ventilation, and air conditioning systems, including specifying and purchasing energy-saving upgrades.

Energy Star Buildings
401 M St. SW
U.S. EPA (6202J)
Washington, DC 20460
202-775-6650
202-233-9659 (fax)

• **Energy Star Computers**
Promotes energy-efficient electronic office equipment by granting use of Energy Star logo to computers, monitors, and printers that meet specifications of low power use. For example, equipment must "power down" after sitting idle to reduce power consumption.

Energy Star Computers
U.S. EPA (6202J)
401 M St. SW
Washington, DC 20460
202-233-9114
202-233-9578 (fax)

• **Environmental Technology Initiative**
Provides grant assistance to promote the development and commercialization of environmental technologies, especially for small businesses.

Innovative Technology Programs
U.S. EPA (8301)
401 M St. SW
Washington, DC 20460
202-260-4073
202-260-3861 (fax)

• **Forest Service Research and Development**
Provides research in industrial technology development to produce and use products that are efficient, safe, and environmentally beneficial. The Forest Service also forms partnerships with businesses to develop new uses for recycled wood, paper, plastic, glass, and metal.

U.S. Forest Service
201 14th St. SW
Washington, DC 20090
202-205-1565
202-205-2497 (fax)

• **Green Lights**
Encourages businesses and institutions to reduce the energy efficiency of their lighting in ways that save money and do not reduce lighting levels. Participants sign a commitment to conduct a lighting audit and upgrade 90 percent of their square footage. Program administrators offer support through workshops, an information hotline, directories, and software to help calculate lighting decisions.

Green Lights
U.S. EPA (6202J)
401 M St. SW
Washington, DC 20460
202-775-6650
202-775-6680 (fax)

• **Innovative Concepts Program**
Provides seed money for the development of energy-efficient technology that is a significant departure from existing technology. Typical grants are $15,000 to $20,000.

Innovative Concepts Program
U.S. Department of Energy
Forrestal Bldg., CE-521
1000 Independence Ave. SW
Washington, DC 20585
202-586-2212
202-586-1605 (fax)

• **Mobility Partners Program**
Information clearinghouse for success stories on innovative transportation programs for communities and businesses. Publishes case studies, technical reports, and a quarterly newsletter of transportation resources for business fleets, commuting, or product distribution system.

Surface Transportation Policy Project
1400 16th St. NW, Ste. 300
Washington, DC 20036
202-939-3470
202-939-3475 (fax)

- **National Industrial Competitiveness through Energy, Environment, Economics (NICE3)**

A joint program of the Energy Department and Environmental Protection Agency to promote energy efficiency, clean production, and economic competitiveness in industry by funding state-industry partnerships for projects development and demonstration. Grants support technology development that can significantly conserve energy and energy-intensive feedstocks, reduce industrial wastes, prevent pollution, and improve industrial cost-competitiveness. Grants of up to $400,000 fund up to 50% of total project cost for up to three years. Applicants must submit project proposals through a state energy, pollution prevention, or business development office.

U.S. Department of Energy
Golden Field Office
1617 Cole Blvd., Bldg. 17
Golden, CO 80401
303-275-4728
303-275-4788 (fax)

- **Small Business Innovation Research**

Awards grants for research and development of pollution control technologies from science- and technology-based firms.

SBIR Program Manager
Office of Exploratory Research (RD-675)
Office of Research and Development
U.S. EPA
401 M St. SW
Washington, DC 20460
202-260-7473
202-260-0211 (fax)

• Small Business Loans and Guarantees for Energy Efficiency
The Small Business Administration grants and guarantees loans of up to $750,000. Energy and Conservation Loans are for equipment purchases, building supplies, and land for an energy-efficient plant. Pollution Control Loans are available for the design, manufacture, and marketing of approved energy-conservation technology.

U.S. Small Business Administration
Office of Business Loans
1441 L St. NW
Washington, DC 20416
800-827-5722
202-606-4225 (fax)

• Stewardship Incentive Program
Provides financial assistance for rural, nonindustrial private landowners (1,000 acres or less) to implement environmentally sound forestry practices. Participants commit to following forest stewardship management plan and may receive up to 75 percent of forest-management practices costs.

Forest Stewardship Program
U.S. Department of Agriculture
P.O. Box 96090, 4th Fl., SE Wing
Washington, DC 20090
202-205-1375
202-205-1271 (fax)

• Technology Transfer
Offers access to 19 EPA laboratories staffed by scientists and engineers. Priorities include pollution prevention, site characterization and remediation technologies, and innovative control technologies.

Federal Technology Transfer Act Coordinator
Office of Science, Planning, and Regulatory Evaluation
U.S. EPA
Cincinnati, OH 45268
513-569-7960
513-569-7132 (fax)

• **WasteWi$e**
Provides technical assistance to companies to reduce solid waste through waste reduction, recycling, and by increasing the purchase or manufacture of recycled products. Participants set their own waste-prevention, recycling, and purchasing goals. Participating companies may use the WasteWi$e logo in advertising.

WasteWi$e
U.S. EPA
401 M St. SW, 5306W
Washington, DC 20460
800-EPA-WISE
703-308-8686 (fax)

• **Water Alliances for Voluntary Efficiency (WAVE)**
Works with businesses to encourage installation of water-efficient equipment wherever practical and profitable. Participants agree to survey their facilities and upgrade inefficient equipment. EPA provides information and software to evaluate opportunities.

WAVE
U.S. EPA
401 M St. SW
Washington, DC 20460
202-260-7288
202-260-1827 (fax)

Federal Pollution Prevention Offices

U.S. EPA Pollution Prevention Program Coordinators
Pollution Prevention Program
U.S. EPA Region 9, H-1-B
75 Hawthorne St.
San Francisco, CA 94105
415-744-2190
415-744-1796 (fax)

Pollution Prevention Resource Center
Pollution Prevention Librarian
U.S. EPA Reg. 9 Library, P-5-3
75 Hawthorne St.
San Francisco, CA 94105
415-744-1508
415-744-1474 (fax)

33/50 Program Coordinator
U.S. EPA Region 9, A-4-4
75 Hawthorne St.
San Francisco, CA 94105
415-744-1061
415-744-1073 (fax)

U.S. EPA Division Contacts
Water Management Division
Pollution Prevention Team
U.S. EPA Region 9, W-2-1
75 Hawthorne St.
San Francisco, CA 94105
415-744-1941
415-744-1078 (fax)

Agriculture Initiative
U.S. EPA Region 9, W-3-1
75 Hawthorne Street
San Francisco, CA 94105
415-744-2009
415-744-1078 (fax)

Air and Toxics Division
Compliance & Enforcement
U.S. EPA Region 9, A-3-1
75 Hawthorne St.
San Francisco, CA 94105
415-744-1205
415-744-1076 (fax)

Pesticides and Toxics
U.S. EPA Region 9, A-4-5
75 Hawthorne St.
San Francisco, CA 94105
415-744-1068
415-744-1073 (fax)

Hazardous Waste Management Division
Waste Minimization Coord.
U.S. EPA Region 9, H-1-W
75 Hawthorne St.
San Francisco, CA 94105
415-744-2153
415-744-1044 (fax)

Solid Waste Section
U.S. EPA Region 9, H-3-1
75 Hawthorne St.
San Francisco, CA 94105
415-744-2091
415-744-1044 (fax)

Green Lights/Global Climate Change Env. Education
U.S. EPA Region 9
75 Hawthorne St.
San Francisco, CA 94105
415-744-1102
415-744-1073 (fax)

Office of Public Affairs
U.S. EPA Region 9, E-2
75 Hawthorne St.
San Francisco, CA 94105
415-744-1581
415-744-1605 (fax)

Federal National Laboratories

Federally sponsored national labs conduct research and most provide technology transfer and commercialization assistance to the private sector. Each lab works in specific areas. For example, Argonne National Lab's specialties include environmental research, waste management, and energy systems analysis.

Argonne National Laboratory
Environmental Sciences
9700 S. Cass Ave., Bldg. 900
Argonne, IL 60439
708-252-3759
708-252-5217 (fax)

Battelle Pacific Northwest Laboratories
P.O. Box 999
Richland, WA 99352
509-375-2139
509-375-2718 (fax)

Brookhaven National Lab
Cornell Ave.
Bldg. 902-C
Upton, NY 11973
516-282-7338
516-282-3729 (fax)

Lawrence Berkeley National Laboratory
1 Cyclotron Rd.
Bldg. 90-1070
Berkeley, CA 94720
516-486-6467
510-486-6457 (fax)

Lawrence Livermore National Laboratory
P.O. Box 808
7000 East Ave., MS L-795
Livermore, CA 94550
510-423-5660
510-423-8988 (fax)

Los Alamos National Lab
Industrial Partnership Office
MS M899
Los Alamos, NM 87545
505-665-2133
505-665-3125 (fax)

Oak Ridge National Laboratory
P.O. Box 2009
Oak Ridge, TN 37831
615-574-0292
615-574-1011 (fax)

Sandia National Laboratories
Technology Transfer and Commercialization Program
P.O. Box 5800, MS 13-80
Albuquerque, NM 87185
505-271-7813
505-271-7867 (fax)

Independent Organizations

• **Business Environmental Assistance Centers**
Provide environmental compliance and technical assistance for state businesses. Sponsor monthly seminars on environmental issues, designed to provide businesses with current regulatory information. Services include one-to-one counseling, assistance in obtaining environmental permits, visits to businesses to help identify measures to be taken, and help in locating financial assistance for pollution-prevention equipment. Provide access to electronic bulletin board system for exchange of information. All services are free. There are two centers covering the northern and southern parts of the state.

Business Environmental Assistance Center
Southern California
100 S. Anaheim Blvd., Ste. 125
Anaheim, CA 92805
800-662-BEAC
714-563-0189 (fax)

Business Environmental Assistance Center
Northern California
3120 de la Cruz Blvd.
Santa Clara, CA 95054
800-799-BEAC
408-748-7388 (fax)

• **Business Environmental Network**
Serves as a clearinghouse of what companies in the San Francisco Bay Area are doing to improve environmental performance. Publishes bimonthly newsletter, *Eco-Opportunities*, and holds regular events to discuss current topics and company policies.

Business Environmental Network
Peninsula Conservation Center
3921 E. Bay Shore Rd.
Palo Alto, CA 94303
415-962-9876
415-962-8234 (fax)

• **Business for Social Responsibility Eco-Efficiency Initiative**
Works with major manufacturers and other companies to develop eco-efficiency projects demonstrating cost savings, productivity gains, and environmental benefits. Promotes business-to-business exchange of successful company initiatives. Conducts training workshops, offers consulting services, and publishes resource materials for companies.

Business for Social Responsibility Education Fund
Eco-Efficiency Initiative
1030 15th St. NW, Ste. 1010
Washington, DC 20005
202-842-5400
202-842-3135 (fax)

• **Buy Recycled Business Alliance**
Helps companies committed increase their purchases of recycled goods. Provides guidance to companies interested in establishing or expanding their in-house "buy recycled" campaigns. Membership includes a newsletter, seminars, and other resources.

Buy Recycled Business Alliance
National Recycling Coalition
1101 30th St. NW, Ste. 305
Washington, DC 20007
202-625-6406
202-625-6409 (fax)

• **California Environmental Business Council**
Promotes California's environmental technology and services industry at the state, national, and international levels. Identifies ways to facilitate export of member goods and services. Works with members for form strategic business partnerships to pursue contract and project opportunities.

California Environmental Business Council
1855 Diamond St., Ste. 5-306
San Diego, CA 92109
619-581-0713
619-581-1280 (fax)

• **California Environmental Business Opportunities (CEBO)**
A joint effort by business, government, academia, and environmental nonprofits to open the California market to businesses that both address critical environmental needs and create significant employment or economic growth opportunities. Helps emerging companies identify the major barriers blocking success, including working with the financial community and regulators to remove barriers.

California Environmental Business Opportunities (CEBO)
Gildea Resource Center
930 Miramonte Dr.
Santa Barbara, CA 93109
805-963-0583
805-962-9080 (fax)

• **California Environmental Technology Center**
A project of the California Environmental Protection Agency and the University of California San Diego Scripps Institution of Oceanography to accelerate the development and commercialization of innovative environmental technologies. The center works with industry experts, national laboratories, federal and state government agencies, universities, private research institutions, and the environmental community.

California Environmental Technology Center
Scripps Institution of Oceanography
9500 Gilman Dr., Mail Code 0241
La Jolla, CA 92093
619-534-8400
619-534-8270 (fax)

• **Californians Against Waste Foundation**
Provides numerous workshops, public education programs, outreach activities, technical assistance, advocacy, and other tools for a sustainable recycling economy. Maintains a database of recycled products. Publications include *Business and Government Buyer's Guide to Recycled Products* and *Guide to Recycled Printing Office Papers*.

Californians Against Waste Foundation
926 J St., Ste. 606
Sacramento, CA 95814
916-443-8317
916-443-3912 (fax)

• **Center for Environmental Economic Development (CEED)**
Assists government, industry, and community groups with the creation of environmentally sound jobs and employment, with a focus on recycling economic development.

Center for Environmental Economic Development
1630 27th St.
Arcata, CA 95521
707-822-8347
707-822-4457 (fax)

• **Centers for Applied Competitive Technologies**
Eight centers located at California community colleges, which aim to increase the state's competitiveness, accelerate technology transfer, and promote continuous quality improvement.

Centers for Applied Competitive Technologies
c/o De Anza College CACT
21250 Stevens Creek Blvd.
Cupertino, CA 95014
408-864-8491
408-864-5441 (fax)

• **Eco Expo and the Green Business Conference**
Annual consumer and industry trade shows (held in Los Angeles in March, Boston in October). Exhibits include a range of consumer and business-to-business products and services; conference topics cover marketing, financing, distribution, and other topics.

Eco Expo
14260 Ventura Blvd., Ste. 201
Sherman Oaks, CA 91423
818-906-2700
818-906-0367 (fax)

• Environmental Business Cluster

Business "incubators" that bring several environmental start-up companies under one roof and provide them with the resources and services to help them flourish. Once accepted into the clusters, companies receive below-market office space, access to research facilities, shared conference rooms, and consulting services.

Environmental Business Cluster
1830 Bering Dr., Ste. 3
San Jose, CA 95112
408-437-5678
408-437-5670 (fax)

• Environmental Compliance Support Association of California

Helps small business owners understand and manage environmental regulations. Offers advice on cost-effective measures to achieve compliance. Operates Helpline, providing information about environmental requirements. AT&T Language Line Services translates for non-English-speaking business owners in 140 languages.

Environmental Compliance Support Association of California
550 S. Hope St., Ste. 2000
Los Angeles, CA 90071
213-627-0456
213-627-0557 (fax)

• Environmental Export Council

A private-sector initiative of corporations, trade associations, and government laboratories formed to expand the export potential of goods and services offered by the environmental technology industry. Helps establish links between companies and foreign markets, target financing opportunities, and sponsors trade missions, international trade exhibitions, and other events.

Environmental Export Council
4140 Oceanside Blvd.
P.O. Box 159-418
Oceanside, CA 92056
619-941-3124
619-941-2419 (fax)

• **E Source**
Information service, originally affiliated with Rocky Mountain Institute, providing independent information on energy-efficient technologies and repeated application issues. Publishes reports, holds conferences and seminars, and provides other services.

E Source
1033 Walnut St.
Boulder, CO 80302
303-440-8500
303-440-8502 (fax)

• **Federal Laboratory Consortium for Technology Transfer**
Comprised of more than 600 member research laboratories and centers from 16 federal departments and agencies. Brings laboratories together with potential users of government-developed technologies and matches potential collaborators with laboratory resources. The consortium's mission is to promote the rapid movement of federal technology research and development into the mainstream U.S. economy.

Federal Laboratory Consortium for Technology Transfer
P.O. Box 545
Sequim, WA 98382
206-683-1005
206-683-6654 (fax)

• **Global Environmental Management Initiative**
Coalition of Fortune 500 companies working to improve environmental performance and stimulate economic growth and sustainable development. Works to apply total quality management tools to corporate environmental management. Sponsors annual conference, publishes workbooks and reports, and conducts workshops.

Global Environmental Management Initiative
2000 L St. NW, Ste. 710
Washington, DC 20036
202-296-7449
202-296-7442 (fax)

- **Institute for Research and Technical Assistance Pollution Prevention Center**

Helps businesses reduce or eliminate use of ozone-depleting substances and chlorinated solvents. Demonstrates and evaluates new materials and processes and helps transfer promising technologies to commercial sector. Provides technical assistance to small and mid-sized companies in the Los Angeles basin and Santa Barbara area.

Institute for Research and Technical Assistance
Pollution Prevention Center
2800 Olympic Blvd., Ste. 101
Santa Monica, CA 90404
310-453-0450
310-453-2660 (fax)

- **Institute of Environmental Solutions**

A nonprofit consortium of state, industry, academic, and nonprofit organizations that forms partnerships to return contaminated land to economic productivity through its Cooperative Solution Program. Offers project design and management, financing development, educational programs, and brokering services.

Institute of Environmental Solutions
717 K St. Mall, Ste. 224
Sacramento, CA 95814
916-444-3412
916-447-3726 (fax)

- **Inventors Workshop International**

Maintains an Eco-Inventors and Entrepreneurs chapter, which assists in the development and commercialization of environmentally related products and services. Helps identify financing and materials sources and provides consultation on marketing, licensing, and intellectual property protection.

Inventors Workshop International
7332 Mason Ave.
Canoga Park, CA 91306
818-340-4268
818-884-8312 (fax)

• Keep California Beautiful
Works with public and private sectors on a wide range of programs to educate business and individuals on solid-waste issues. Projects include training and education in the workplace, including recycling and source-reduction program development and initiatives to address grassroots efforts toward litter- and graffiti-prevention challenges. (See also local affiliate listings, beginning on page 64.)

Keep California Beautiful
1601 Exposition Blvd., FB 15
Sacramento, CA 95815
800-CLEAN-CA
916-924-5667
916-920-8119 (fax)

• Materials for the Future Foundation
Provides grants and loans to nonprofit organizations in the recovered-materials industry and supports community-based economic development related to recycling. Project areas include training and technical assistance, resource development, policy development, public education, and research and information.

Materials for the Future Foundation
1230 Preservation Park
Oakland, CA 94612
510-465-6333
510-465-4954 (fax)

• National Technology Transfer Center
Promotes the transfer of federally funded research to U.S. businesses. Provides free consultation to companies searching for specific technologies through access to data bases, laboratories, and other resources.

National Technology Transfer Center
316 Washington Ave.
Wheeling, WV 26003
800-243-2455
304-243-2510
304-243-2539 (fax)

• **Recycled Paper Coalition**
Encourages paper recycling and purchase of paper made from recycled material. Organized by several San Francisco-area companies, including Bank of America, Pacific Gas & Electric, and Chevron Corp.

Recycled Paper Coalition
c/o Peninsula Conservation Center
3921 E. Bayshore Rd.
Palo Alto, CA 94303
415-962-9876
415-962-8234 (fax)

• **U.S. Green Building Council**
Supports improved energy and environmental efficiency for commercial, industrial, and residential buildings. Works with government and private-sector organizations to originate and accelerate standards for building design and construction. Hosts educational programs for member companies and the public.

U.S. Green Building Council
7900 Wisconsin Ave., Ste. 404
Bethesda, MD 20814
301-657-3469
301-907-9326 (fax)

Energy Utility Programs

• **Sacramento Municipal Utility District**
Offers a range of energy-efficiency programs for business, including commercial/industrial load-management programs and retrofits. A solar power program awards contracts to boost California's photovoltaic industry. A cogeneration program buys excess power produced on industrial sites.

Sacramento Municipal Utility District
P.O. Box 15830
Sacramento, CA 95852
916-732-5494 (energy services)
916-732-5695 (fax)
916-732-6679 (solar power)
916-732-5695 (fax)
916-732-6724 (cogeneration)
916-732-6771 (fax)

- **Pacific Gas & Electric Company**

Offers a variety of financial incentives for commercial, industrial and agricultural, and multifamily customers who install energy-efficient equipment. Through Capital Advantage program, provides reduced-interest-rate financing for up to 100% of the cost of energy-efficiency measures. Offers energy information to commercial customers to identify appropriate energy-efficiency upgrades.

Pacific Gas & Electric Company
Energy Efficient Resource Center
1919 Webster St.
Oakland, CA 94612
800-468-4743, ext. 665
510-763-1568 (fax)

- **Los Angeles Department of Water and Power**

Operates an Energy Management Partnership to reduce energy consumption and peak demand. Services include energy accounting and assessment to track and analyze energy use; operations and maintenance assistance consultation; technical assistance for remodeling, retrofitting, and construction; and financial incentives for installing energy-efficiency equipment.

Los Angeles Department of Water and Power
333 S. Beaudry, Rm. 1745
Los Angeles, CA 90017
800-U-ASK-DWP
213-481-3266
213-481-5911 (fax)

• Southern California Gas Company
Energy Management Services Program and Equipment Replacement and Process Modernization Program provide commercial and industrial customers with energy audits, financial incentives for replacing and upgrading appliances, and air quality assistance.

Southern California Gas Company
Commercial-Industrial Sales Staff
1919 S. State College Blvd.
Anaheim, CA 92806
800-GAS-2000
213-244-1200
213-244-8261 (fax)

• Southern California Edison
Offers a range of support programs, helping companies reduce emissions and hazardous waste, and encouraging energy-efficiency upgrades, green purchasing policies, solid-waste reduction, and telecommuting. Operates Customer Technology Application Center, providing information about new technologies and products for business, industry, commercial, and residential applications.

Southern California Edison
6090 N. Irwindale Ave.
Irwindale, CA 91702
818-812-7380
818-812-7381 (fax)

• San Diego Gas and Electric
Provides energy-efficiency programs for commercial, industrial, and agricultural programs, including information programs, energy-management services, energy-efficiency incentives, new construction consultation, and load-management consultation.

San Diego Gas and Electric
8306 Century Park Ct., Ste. 6201
San Diego, CA 92123
800-336-SDGE
619-239-7511
619-654-1755 (fax)

About the Author

Joel Makower, a native of Oakland, is a writer and lecturer on business and environmental topics, and editor of *The Green Business Letter.* A graduate in journalism of the University of California at Berkeley, he is author, co-author, or editor of more than a dozen books. Titles include *The E-Factor: The Bottom-Line Approach to Environmentally Responsible Business* (1993), on how companies are responding to environmental challenges in positive and profitable ways; *The Green Consumer* (1990; revised, 1993), an authoritative reference on environmental consumerism; *50 Simple Things Your Business Can Do to Save the Earth* (1991); and *Beyond the Bottom Line: Putting Social Responsibility to Work for Your Business and the World* (1994), about the profit and potential of socially responsible business practices. His weekly column, "The Green Consumer," is syndicated nationally by Universal Press Syndicate. Makower is a regular commentator on green business topics for "Marketplace," a nightly national business program on public radio, and lectures internationally to companies, industry groups, and business schools. He lives and works in Washington, D.C.